DOODLE ANIMALS

Buster Books

Illustrated by Emma Parrish

'Doodle Animals' contains new material, and material selected from 'Doodle Farm' and 'Doodle Zoo', previously published in 2010 by Buster Books.

This book was first published in 2012.
Buster Books is an imprint of Michael O'Mara Books Limited,
9 Lion Yard, Tremadoc Road, London SW4 7NQ
www.mombooks.com/busterbooks

ISBN: 978-1-78055-016-9

2 4 6 8 10 9 7 5 3 1

This book was printed in November 2011
by Shenzhen Wing King Tong Paper Products Co. Ltd., Shenzhen, Guangdong, China.

Papers used by Buster Books are natural, recyclable products made from wood grown in sustainable forests. The manufacturing processes conform to the environmental regulations of the country of origin.

What has hatched from the egg?

Draw humps on these camels. One hump or two?

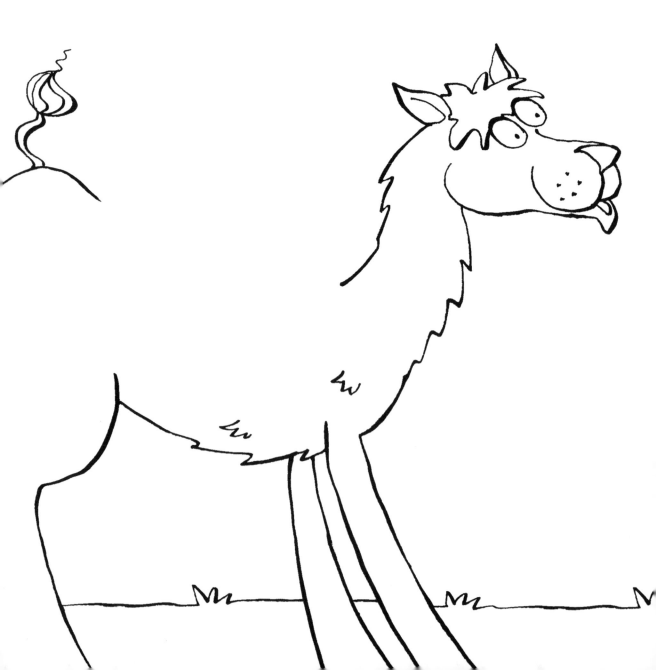

What is the grizzly bear dreaming about?

Fill the pond with happy hippos.

Draw more hummingbirds and
give them lots of flowers to drink from.

Give these parrots brightly coloured, long tail feathers.

Give this snake a shiny new skin.

Fill the branch with sleeping bats.

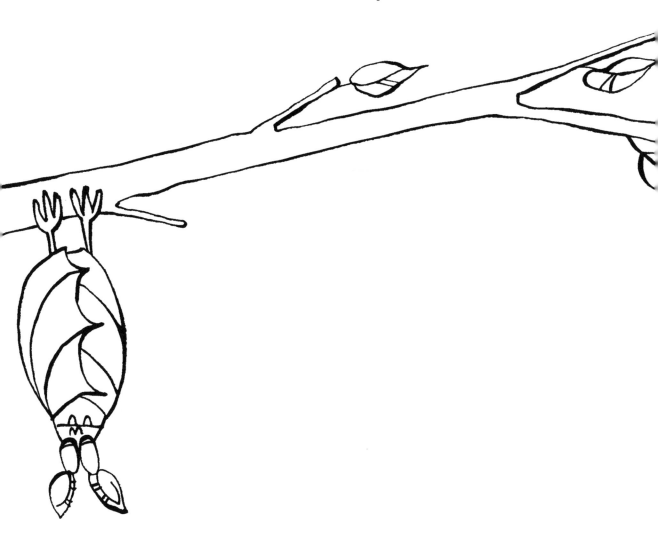

Fill the crocodile's mouth with sharp teeth.

What is he about to gobble up?

Give the chimp
a pile of bananas.

Fill the page with buzzing bees.

Draw lots of juicy bugs for the chameleons to eat.

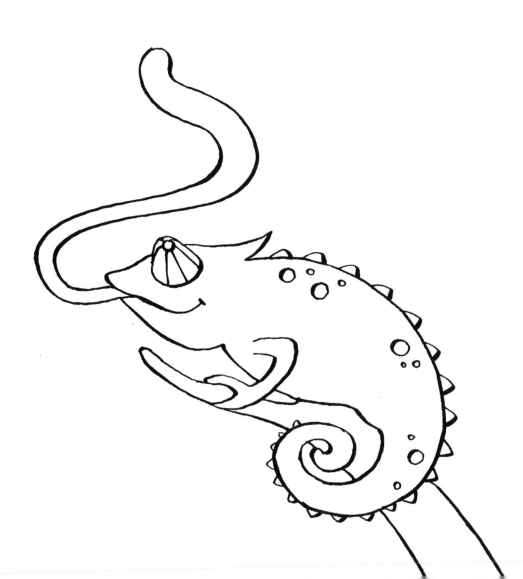

Give these lions magnificent manes.

Fill the bucket with tasty fish for the penguin.

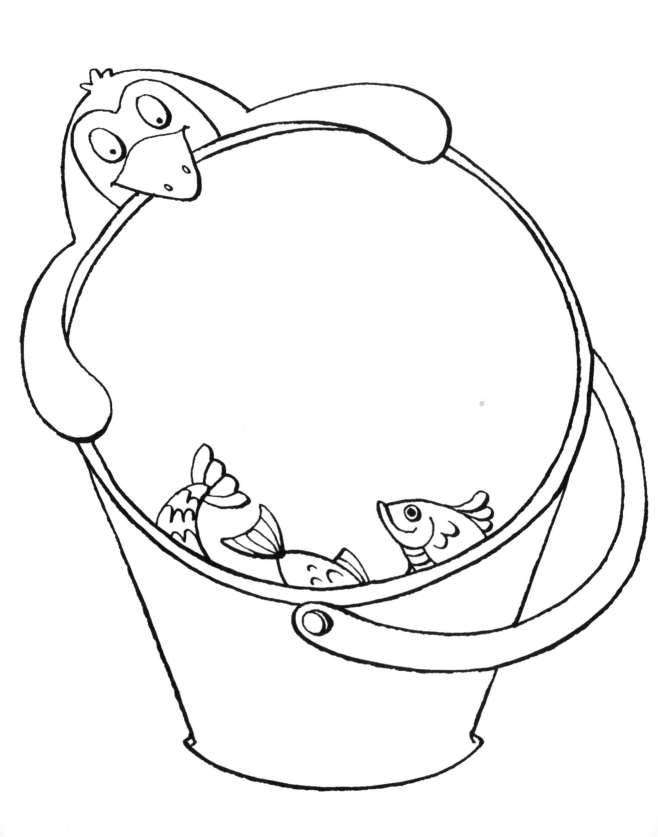

Give these two toucans big, brightly coloured beaks.

Give the ring-tailed lemurs long, stripy tails.

Fill the page with beautiful butterflies.

Put more spots on this leopard . . .

. . . and more stripes on this tiger.

Give these monkeys something fun to swing on.

Fill the wire with pairs of lovebirds.

Fill the page with snakes and give them rattles on their tails.

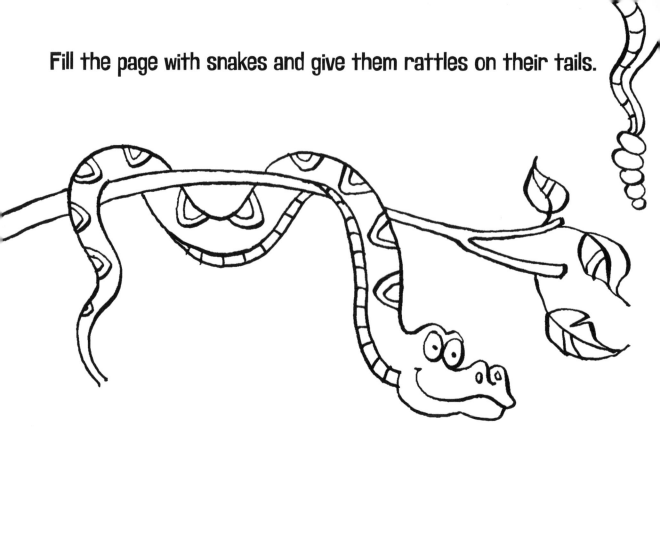

Add patterns to the giant tortoise's shell.

Finish the big tree to shade the sleeping lion.

Fill the sea with starfish . . .

. . . and lots of seahorses, too.

What is in the pond?

Fill this pond with frogs and frogspawn.

Fill the basket with more kittens.

Fill the pigsty with little piglets. Don't forget their curly tails.

Draw a jumble of jellyfish.

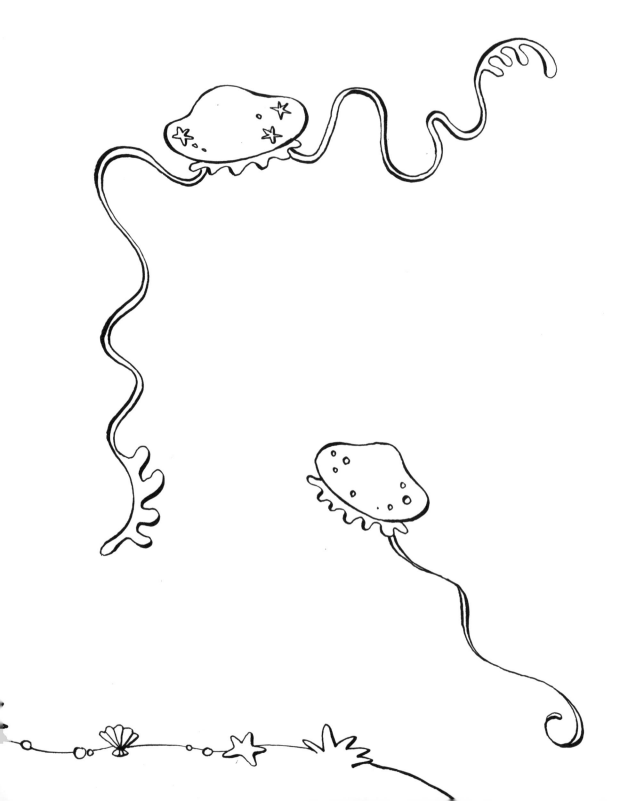

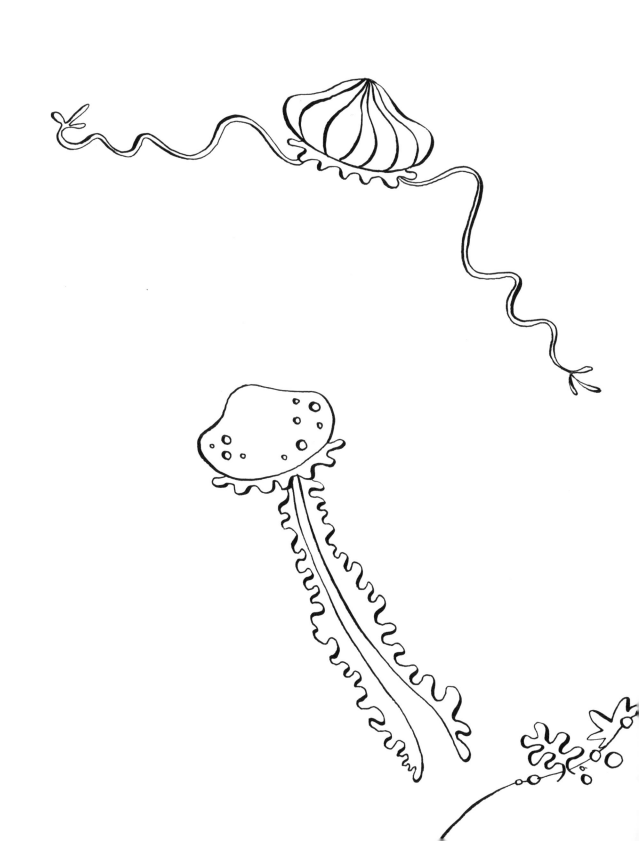

What is the shark attacking?

Fill the sea with fish of all shapes and sizes.

Who is riding the horses?

Draw lots of bamboo shoots for the panda to eat.

Give the elephant big ears.

Draw more walruses on the ice.

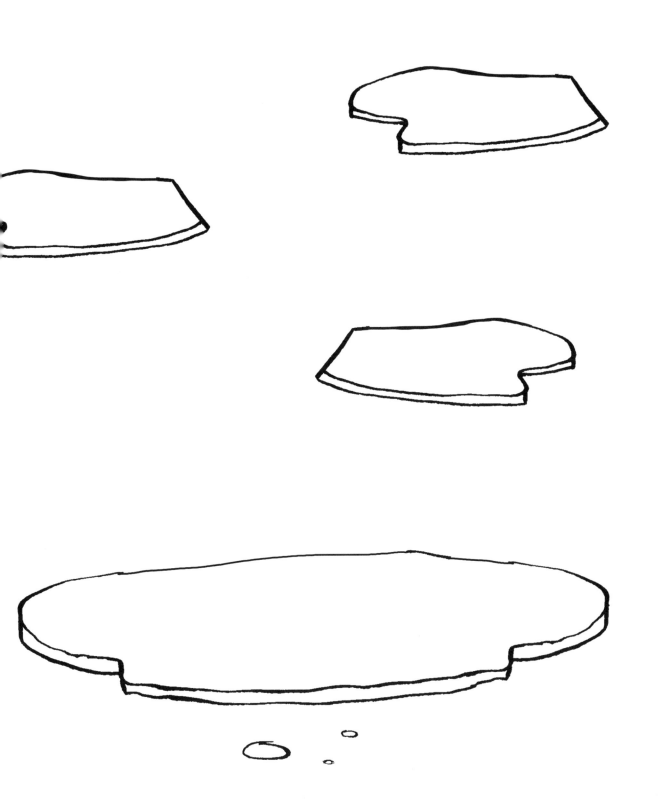

Can you draw a flock of sheep with funny haircuts?

Draw some more cows in the field . . .

. . . and give them black splodges
on their coats.

Fill this page with your favourite animals.

PET BIRDS

Questions and Answers

by Christina Mia Gardeski

raintree

a Capstone company — publishers for children

Raintree is an imprint of Capstone Global Library Limited, a company incorporated in England and Wales having its registered office at 264 Banbury Road, Oxford, OX2 7DY – Registered company number: 6695582

www.raintree.co.uk
myorders@raintree.co.uk

Edited by Carrie Braulick Sheely and Alesha Halvorson
Designed by Kayla Rossow
Picture research by Pam Mitsakos
Production by Gene Bentdahl

ISBN 978 1 4747 2141 7 (hardback)
20 19 18 17 16
10 9 8 7 6 5 4 3 2 1

ISBN 978 1 4747 2153 0 (paperback)
21 20 19 18 17
10 9 8 7 6 5 4 3 2 1

British Library Cataloguing in Publication Data
A full catalogue record for this book is available from the British Library.

Every effort has been made to contact copyright holders of material reproduced in this book. Any omissions will be rectified in subsequent printings if notice is given to the publisher.

All the internet addresses (URLs) given in this book were valid at the time of going to press. However, due to the dynamic nature of the internet, some addresses may have changed, or sites may have changed or ceased to exist since publication. While the author and publisher regret any inconvenience this may cause readers, no responsibility for any such changes can be accepted by either the author or the publisher.

Acknowledgements
Alamy: Ashley Cooper, 4-5, Elena Abduramanova, 15, Eudyptula, 13, kungverylucky, 7, Tracy Starr, 11, Ulyana Vyugina, 19, VladisChern, 1, 22, Yuangeng Zhang, cover, zhuda, 21, Zurijeta, 17; Thinkstock: einegraphic, 9, moodboard, 10

Printed and bound in China.